Published and distributed by

 ISLAND HERITAGE
P  U  B  L  I  S  H  I  N  G

94-411 KŌʻAKI STREET, WAIPAHU, HAWAIʻI   96797
Orders: (800) 468-2800  •  Information: (808) 564-8800
Fax: (808) 564-8877
islandheritage.com

ISBN:0-89610-502-4
First Edition, First Printing, 2003

Designed by Danvers Fletcher

# *Proteas*
## IN HAWAI'I

By Paul Wood / Photographs by Ron Dahlquist

### ISLAND HERITAGE

# Acknowledgments

Mahalo (thanks) to David Oka and Pam Shingaki of the
Maui Agricultural Research Center, a facility of the University of
Hawai'i College of Tropical Agriculture and Human Resources.
Also thanks to Jim Heid and Linda Puppolo of Kula Vista Protea
and Corintha Pohle of Valley View Protea Farm.

# Contents

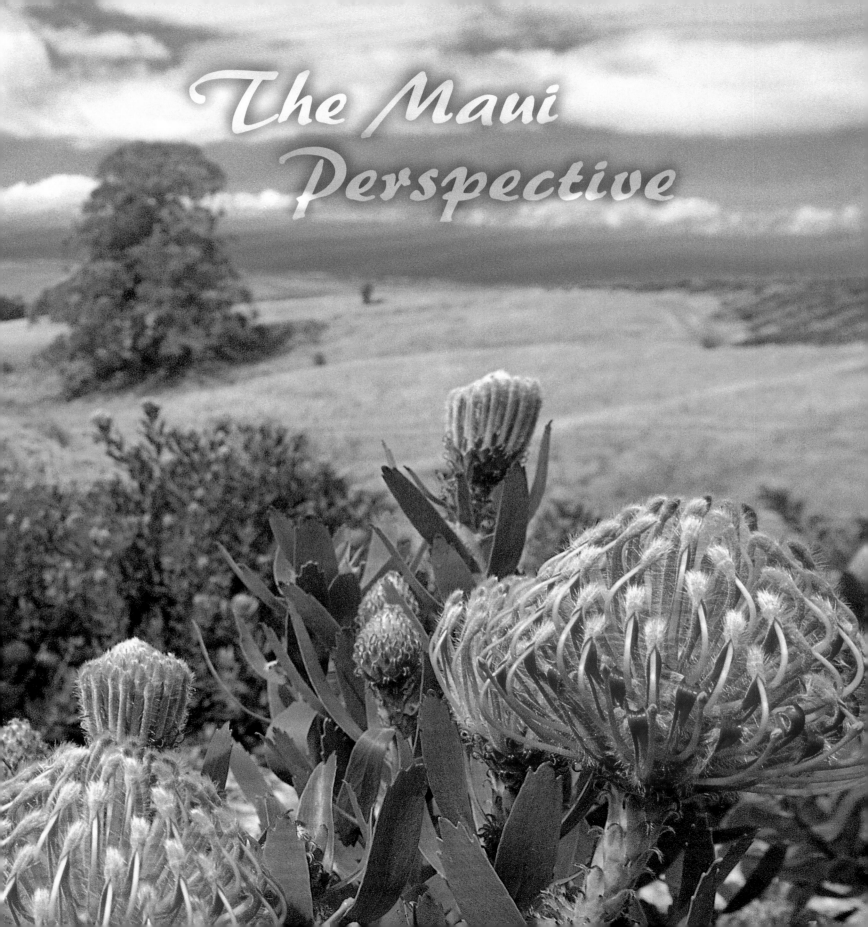

# The Maui
# Perspective

East Maui's Kula district is a cool foothills region dedicated to farming and ranching. A jacaranda tree blossoms in the foreground as Haleakalā, a dormant volcano, rises in the distance.

On the island of Maui, where I live, certain kinds of marvels are commonplace. A moonshine rainbow will merit a glance or two as we drive down the mountain to see a movie, but a three-foot swell might not be good enough to justify waxing the old surfboard. When a fruit-heavy banana stalk crashes down into our blooming ginger patch, we sigh at the magnitude of the gardening chore. Maybe this year we forgot to watch the Merrie Monarch Hula Festival, or we were just too busy to show up for an Aloha Festivals concert. It's not that we're insensitive, but we are—well, human.

Recently I saw a pickup truck tooling through Makawao loaded with proteas. It looked as though somebody had plucked a fireworks display out of the sky, tossed the explosions in the back of the truck, and driven off—a one-vehicle parade. But nobody gave it a second glance. Everyone was busy dealing with the mundane affairs of life—darting into the general store for laulaus and sashimi, getting the kids to their hula lesson or dodging the long line of tourists on bicycles who had just coasted all the way down from the 10,000-foot summit of Haleakalā.

*TOP: The little crossroads town of Makawao is a social hub of Maui's protea-growing region.*
*BOTTOM: Farm workers get a truckload of leucospermums ready for local delivery.*

7

Proteas thrive in this particular band of the mountain, the district called Kula whose sloping landscape of fertile volcanic soil between the 2,000- and 4,000-foot elevation is blessed with warm

days, cool nights, dry summers and generous seaborne breezes—just the right conditions for these little-known Southern-Hemisphere natives. Kula has always been farming country, and the neighborhoods and open grassy fields are interrupted here and there by truck farms specializing in cabbage, carnations, string beans, and sweet Maui onions. It's ranching country, too, with its own colorful paniolo (Hawaiian cowboy) traditions.

So when proteas come through town, we recognize them as a familiar part of the landscape. They're similar in size to the monstrous tropicals—the heliconia, torch ginger, and bird-of-paradise—that people haul into town from Maui's windward jungles. We forget how rare and sensational proteas are in the eyes of the world. I even heard someone say recently, "Proteas are kind of boring."

*Working under blue Hawaiian skies, a harvester strips the stems of the popular king protea,* Protea cynaroides. *Within hours these blossoms will be boxed and on their way around the world.*

Boring! That's like saying, "Ho hum, another expedition to Annapurna."

Thank goodness Maui has tourists. They help us stay attuned to the wonder of proteas. When visitors see a protea, they marvel, "What in heaven's name is THAT? Is it real? What planet did it come from?"

The planet that proteas come from is our own, of course. They are significant reminders that earthly life is both powerful and beautiful. In fact, these exuberant blossoms are not tricked in laboratories or forced by hormones into their giant effects. The Earth itself produced these magnificent blooms, using simple materials such as crumbled granite, abundant sun, and an occasional dusting of rain.

Proteas are naturally occurring species. The new varieties— and our protea growers work with the University of Hawai'i to develop new varieties every year—give nature's design subtle alterations, such as longer stems, color enhancements, or a bit more resistance to diseases.

When you bring a bouquet of proteas home, perhaps bumping aside the daisies and the African violets, you are making a statement about the joy of the Earth. The message of these spectacular flowers can be summed up in one phrase: Hallelujah for life.

And the message persists for months, even years, if you choose. Unlike most other flowers, proteas endure long after they've stopped sipping water in the vase. They dry beautifully, maintaining their form and to some extent their color.

It is my wish that this book, featuring images by master photographer Ron Dahlquist, will not only provide fascinating tidbits about these plants but also add to your sense of wonder about them.

*This "pincushion" protea,* Leucospermum reflexum *var.* 'luteum,*' is a pale yellow sport of a naturally occurring orange flower.*

# Messengers from Gondwanaland

When botanists began studying the family of plants that we call proteas, they found themselves staring at a riddle. Reasonable attempts to explain this riddle have validated an outlandish theory about the history of our planet.

To understand this riddle, you need some information about the family, which is properly called Proteaceae. It's a good-sized family that

*The banksias evolved in Australia. This one,* Banksia baxteri, *is a prolific bloomer. Its relatively small flowers and short foliage make it a standard of the cut-flower trade.*

has proven to be quite successful at adapting to the challenges of earthly life. Scientists have identified 75 genera—that is, 75 solid variations on the family theme—and more than 1,000 distinct species. The family's natural distribution is quite widespread, all of it occurring in tropical and subtropical regions south of the equator. You'll find proteas growing naturally in tropical Africa, South America, Malaya, New Zealand, and some Pacific islands, but the primary concentrations of protea are found in two places—South Africa and Australia. Therein lies the riddle.

The family members in these two places are clearly proteas. In other words, the details of flower and seed structure are so similar to each other and so distinct from other plant formulas that nobody questions the shared heredity of these two groups. Even so, the two groups are as different from each other as tennis from ping-pong. Not one species of South African proteas ever got to Australia on its own, and vice versa. Even the genera—the family's long-evolved tribes—are completely different in the two regions. In fact, this family is split so profoundly that botanists have divided the proteas into two subfamilies. The "proteoids" populated South Africa and spread to some extent north on that continent. The "grevilleoids" spread across Australia, and their kind worked their way north in that part of the world.

The question is obvious: How did proteas get to two places that are separated by 4,000 miles of open sea? And let's not overlook the fact that some proteas got to South America—an equally formidable sea crossing from either Africa or Australia. The seeds of protea are unfit for such travels. They don't float, nor can they blow through the air any distance, nor are they eaten or carried by seagoing birds.

It would be easy to suppose that human beings carried seeds around in their restless voyaging. (Stone Age florists, perhaps?) But this idea fails in light of Darwin's theory of evolution, which is accepted to some degree by virtually all scientists.

As you probably know, Darwin suggested that life is a constantly changing process. If you take two populations of the same species and separate them in two different environments, over a period of time they will start to look and act different from each other. In, say, five thousand years they will be different a little bit. In five million years, they will be extremely different.

In fact, it takes millions of years for plants to grow as far apart as proteoids from grevilleoids. In other words, the fact that the two protea

*The king protea,* Protea cynaroides, *will always be the crowning achievement of evolution in the rugged hills of South Africa.*

groups separated at the subfamily level tells scientists that the separation happened a long, long time ago—long before human beings evolved to build canoes and to ship bouquets. So the proteas must have jumped continents by themselves.

Or—and here's the outlandish theory—the continents moved. What if Australia and Africa were one body of land at one time, but broke apart, like a raft splitting in two? One land mass went hither; the other went yon. And, of course, they carried their proteas with them.

In fact, continents do drift. They float around slowly on the molten core of the Earth. The Hawaiian Islands, for example, are creeping closer to Russia at the rate of four inches a year. And the slow trajectory that scientists have measured between Australia and Africa suggests that those continents could have been stuck together once. Advocates of this theory have come up with a name for this ancient supercontinent—Gondwanaland.

So the strange distribution of the protea family seems to verify the measurements of continental drift. Not only that, the fact that Australia and South America share about half their genera of grevilleoids suggests a refinement of this idea. South America was part of Gondwanaland, too. After the breakup, South America and Australia hung together for quite a while—long enough for several genera to evolve—before parting ways.

People often suggest that proteas have a prehistoric look to them. That's not fair because nearly all the plants familiar to us are "prehistoric." But the word makes poetic sense when you think of the proteas' role as messengers from Gondwanaland.

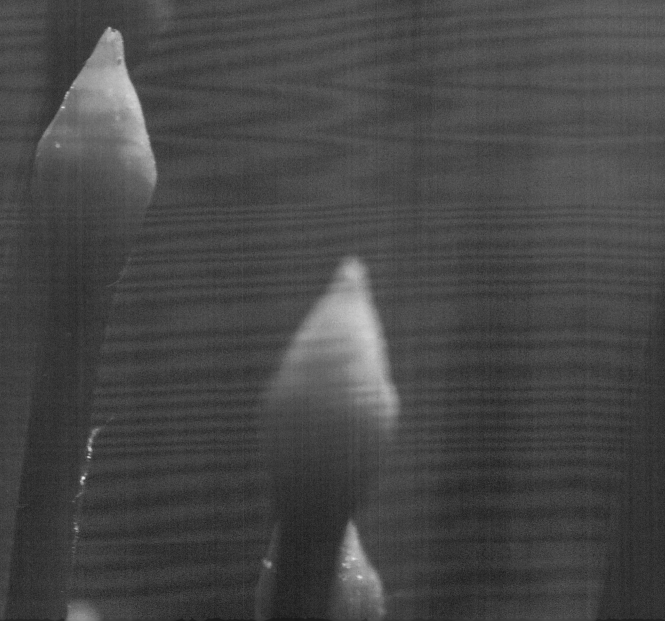

Botanically
Speaking

Most of us can talk our way through the basic parts of a flower.
Take a rose, for example. It's fairly easy to find the petals, which
collectively are called the flower's corolla. When you look
underneath the petals, you can spot the green sepals. These
enclose and protect the flower bud when it's young and then,
when the petals burst open like popcorn, the sepals curl back,
their job done. Collectively the sepals are called the flower's
calyx. To talk about the corolla and the calyx combined, scientists use the word "perianth"—the material that surrounds (peri)
the flower (anth).

Now open the rose blossom and look at the working
flower components inside. The first thing you notice are an
abundance of wiry stems, the stamens. At the tip of each stamen
is a tiny rice-grain-shaped object called an anther. These anthers
exude a golden sticky dust called pollen, the magic male pow-
der. The wiry stems on which the anthers stand are called
filaments.

In the center of all these stamens, like a queen bee among
her host of attendants, sits the female part, the pistil. The base of
the pistil is a green globe called the ovary. This will get fertilized
by the pollen and ripen into the fruit, the rose hip, which will
make seeds for the next generation. But the pollen has to get to
the future fruit through a delivery system that rises from the top

*FAR LEFT: This leucospermum blossom
shows what happens when a protea flower
matures. The wiry styles reflex, or pop.
Each style represents a different flower in
the crowded, geometrically organized
inflorescence.*
*ABOVE: In some proteas, such as this
Banksia coccinea, the styles have a devil of
a time trying to reflex.*

*Young and old. The leucospermum flower above is still reflexing, with many of its young styles (the female structures) still trapped in the center. Below, the mature flower has all of its styles reflexed, leaving the stamens (the male structures) to adorn the diminutive flower parts, or perianths. FAR RIGHT: The drama builds as the styles of this leucospermum bow outward, straining to reflex.*

of the ovary. This delivery system has two parts—the style, which is simply a stem reaching up to the sky (in a rose, the style is very short, almost negligible) and some kind of frilly or knobby structure above to capture the pollen. This structure is called the stigma.

This whole floral device sits on a base that scientists call the receptacle. In a rose the receptacle is quite small, but please remember the term.

Basic botany. With this vocabulary, you can look at a flower and say, "I see...."

But when even the most observant person looks at a protea, his first reaction is normally, "Huh?" Basic structures don't seem to apply. And yet the basic structures are there. The following explanation will help you get familiar with the protea's floral anatomy. Why? Because when all you can say is, "Huh?" you're missing half the fun of a flower—the botanist's fun.

A protea possesses the same parts as a rose, but the prominent parts of the rose have shrunk, and the lesser parts have assumed dominant roles. Take the receptacle, for example—the floral base. In every protea the receptacle grows into a wide round plate on which innumerable tiny flowers sit. Even though protea blossoms can be huge, single protea flowers are actually rather obscure. It is only when the flowers form a committee that they take on their visual splendor. (By the way, this collective approach to flower making also was adopted by an entirely different plant group, the Composites, which includes the

sunflower, daisy, marigold, and artichoke.)

In a protea, the petals so prominent in a rose have dwindled to nothing but nectar sacks for attracting birds. The little flower's dominating feature is its pistil (the female reproductive stem), which it flings out into the open air. For this purpose, unlike the pistil on a rose, the protea's pistil has a very long, brightly colored style. When the whole blossom is completely mature, all the sprout-like styles have popped out, forming the "pincushion" effect. But this popping out takes a fair amount of work. While the flower is young, the style is trapped temporarily inside a sheath made from the perianth—the collective flower parts all fused together—which restrains the style long enough to coat it with pollen. In some species the tension of the trapped style is so great that the styles arc outward and back, like embroidered loops.

When you look down through the crowd of flowers on a single protea blossom, you see a spiral pattern of geometrical perfection. The central flowers are younger than the perimeter ones, so they are slower to pop forth. As the whole blossom ages, the receptacle continues to grow and harden, sometimes forming a handsome woody cone. In time, each successful

*TOP: The knobs at the ends of these "pincushion" styles are ripe and ready to receive the fertilizing effect of pollen. BOTTOM: In a crowded protea inflorescence, flowers are arranged in a spiral pattern of geometrical perfection.*

protea flower develops a single hard-shelled seed. These seeds are often covered in fuzz, or they are slightly winged, or they are simple and nut-shaped like pine nuts. When a blossom rippens and dries, you can pull the seeds off the receptacle for a simpler dried-flower effect.

We've come this far without mentioning the most garish floral structure of this plant family, a structure peculiar to just one of its tribes. The spectacular king proteas and any blossom from the genus *Protea* provide envelopes for their flower-committees. As if trying to return to the simple effect of the rose, these plants encase the entire blossom in brightly colored, hard, petal-like bracts. Collectively, the bracts of a single blossom are called an involucre. The involucre is attractive, just as a rose's corolla. Unlike rose petals, though, these bracts persist, hold their color, and contribute to the everlasting quality of flowers of the genus *Protea*.

The flower details described above characterize the plant family called Proteaceae. Please do not despair of pronouncing

ABOVE: Flowers of the genus Protea have an added feature—the brightly colored involucre, or circling cup of showy bracts. Shown here is the 'Lady Di' protea, a natural hybrid from South Africa.

*ABOVE:  Proteas of the genus Leucadendron discriminate by gender— some plants are male, some female. But this group is prized less for its flowers than for the brilliant, graceful foliage that tops each flowering stem.*

*RIGHT: Generally speaking, proteas build a large blossom by massing many small flowers on a single thick receptacle.  Flowers of the genus Banksia take this plan to the extreme.  They grow the receptacle into a long, club-like cone.  Shown here is B. menziesii.*

this complicated-looking but easy word. Every plant family name ends with the sound of three letters pronounced in a row: A, C, E. So when we talk about "proteas" with a lower-case "p," we mean every plant in the family pronounced PRO-TEE-A-C-E.

In botanical language the "–aceae" ending is always added onto the name of the "type genus"—the genus that botanists have chosen as the best representative of the characteristics of this family. The rose family, *Rosaceae*, is named for the genus *Rosa*. The proteas are named for the genus *Protea*, which

includes the king protea, the national flower of South Africa. The proteas also include the other genera grown in Hawai'i, which are illustrated in Chapter Five entitled "The Protea Tribes"—*Leucospermum*, *Leucadendron*, and *Banksia*.

Besides the floral beauties described in Chapter Five, the Proteacea includes two groups that might be familiar to you. The genus *Grevillea*, which hails from Australia and New Caledonia, includes several species of flowering shrubs and trees that have entered the nursery trade. In Hawai'i, two grevilleas have escaped from cultivation and established themselves in the natural landscape. One of these is a slender tree named *Grevillea banksii*. Locally we call this the kāhili flower or the haiku tree—because it was first introduced to

Hawai'i in the Maui district of Ha'ikū. The other is *Grevillea robusta*, the silk oak or silver oak, which is commonly planted throughout the world's tropical and subtropical regions. In Kula this attractive runaway with its golden flowers blooms just in time to harmonize with the area's many violet-flowered jacarandas.

Another protea is grown in Hawai'i for its meaty nut—the macadamia (*Macadamia integrifolia*). Brightly packaged, canned, boxed, flavored, smoked, and toasted variations have made macadamia nuts a signature crop of the Islands, far from the tree's native land Down Under.

One final point about pronunciation of the word "protea." You hear people say pro-TAY-a, with the accent on the second syllable. This mispronunciation has become so common in Hawai'i that you hear the flower growers themselves alternate it with the correct pronunciation—PRO-tee-a, accent on the first syllable. The family is named for the Greek god Proteus (PRO-tee-us), who could change his shape at will and take on fantastic forms.

# The Fynbos Homeland

To truly appreciate the proteas of Hawai'i, we need to make an imaginary visit to South Africa. Most of the flowers that wind up in your protea bouquet originated naturally in a rare and peculiar landscape—a landscape that shaped the plants and that travels with them, in a way, to the vase in your living room.

Cape of Good Hope is the name the old sailors gave to the blunt southern tip of the African continent that pushes into the wild seas and divides the southern Atlantic Ocean from the Indian Ocean. Here a swath of rugged, folded granite mountains forms a barrier against the impact of the ocean, like a cowcatcher on a locomotive. It's as if the Cape is defended by a curving rampart of mountains three rows deep, sweeping in a five-hundred-mile curve between the settlements of Clanwilliam and Grahamstown. The relatively dry, treeless peaks form a dramatic backdrop to the seacoast cities of Cape Town and Port Elizabeth.

A folded, pocketed, tough terrain, these mountains provided nature with a multitude of hatching places for fourteen different genera and more than three hundred species of the protea family. Separated from each other by such complex topography, isolated populations developed unique identities. But all of them needed to adapt to the same rigorous conditions—dry, hot periods and lots of wind. Although plants on these slopes do not have to contend with deep winter chill, they do have to cope with drought and exposure.

The early Dutch settlers in the Cape region invented their own name for this landscape. Fynbos, they called it—"fine bush."

Ecologists would describe the region with the word "macchia" and note that similar habitats occur in discreet areas where the same conditions apply—for example, the Mediterranean coast of southern France, the chaparral country of California, the mulga region of Australia, the dry scrubland of Chile, and the Kula slopes of Maui. It won't surprise you to learn that farmers in all these fynbos-like areas have taken up the cultivation of proteas for the cut-flower trade.

The nature of the fynbos explains why proteas are heavier and more robust than orchids, lilies, or carnations. It also explains the drought-resistant qualities that make proteas such long-lived cut flowers and such everlasting dried flowers. But nothing can explain the amazing confidence of these plants. Proteas proclaim an exuberance for life that goes far beyond the mere will to survive.

To imagine the homeland of proteas, picture steep, rocky slopes under a clean, bare sky. Everywhere, broken clusters of dark granite protrude from the soil, badged with lichens. Tucked in around these stones are thickets of hardy green foliage. At regular intervals, these shrubs ripen into explosions of undaunted color as if to say, "Nothing can stop me. The fynbos is my homeland. The Earth is my home."

*Maui protea grower Jim Heid snapped this image and the one on pages 28-29 while on a research trip to the protea homeland of South Africa. He was caught by the landscape's similarity to scenes in Hawai'i, especially O'ahu's Diamond Head. Ron Dahlquist's image on page 30 shows a South Africa scene near Lesotho.*

# The Protea Tribes

Because their hatching grounds are all located so far from Europe, proteas didn't get into the hands of Western scientists until relatively modern times. The first to describe and name them was Carolus Linnaeus himself in 1735. Linneaus, the brilliant Swedish naturalist who invented our system of scientific nomenclature, received a shipment of plant specimens from the Cape region and found himself staring in amazement. Although he could see that the basic flower formula was the same in each plant, their variety of physical expressions went far beyond his normal experience in the land of apples and tulips. In a moment of poetic inspiration, Linnaeus named the group after the Greek god Proteus—a sea god who could evade a hero's grasp by changing his shape into all manner of startling forms.

During the eighteenth and nineteenth centuries proteas were favorites in the greenhouses of European royalty. In 1881 Sir Joseph Hooker, director of England's royal Kew Gardens, wrote that proteas are "the handsomest of plants, whether for size, form or colour of inflorescence; and would carry away the first prize at any horticultural show." At the same time, he complained about "the introduction of those improved systems of heating houses and that incessant watering, that favours soft-wooded plants, and is death to the Proteas of South Africa and the Banksias of Australia." In other words, new hothouse technology was creating steamy, orchid-favoring indoor jungles, and the proteas were simply rotting away.

*FAR LEFT: Bouquets typically combine flowers of four genera:* Protea, Leucospermum, Leucadendron, *and* Banksia.

35

For a while, these plants faded from the attention of Northern-Hemisphere gardeners.

Although nature has provided us with seventy-five genera of Proteaceae, only four of the groups are commonly represented in the bouquets shipped from farms in Hawai'i. New varieties are being introduced all the time, but the four dominant tribes are here to stay, and they are easy to recognize: the genus Protea, the genus Leucospermum, the genus Leucadendron, and the genus Banksia.

*This "duchess" type protea goes by the name 'Sylvia.' The "duchess" proteas show their derivation from Protea eximea in that their bracts are spoon-shaped—narrower at the base. This flower is a natural hybrid from South Africa, a cross between P. eximea and P. susannae.*

*ABOVE: Protea 'Susara' is a South African cultivar that results from the crossing of P. magnifica and P. susannae.*
*FAR RIGHT: In 1976 Protea cynaroides, the king protea, was declared the national plant of South Africa. Flower heads can grow more than twelve inches across, although six or seven inches is the norm.*
*RIGHT: Protea aristata makes a good landscaping plant, growing four to six feet tall. It blooms early in the season. The needle-like leaves have a strong, sulfurous smell.*

# Protea

The genus *Protea* is the largest and most widespread group of the family Proteaceae, with eighty-two species in the country of South Africa alone.

The dominant trait of the genus *Protea*, evident at a glance, is what a botanist would call a "decorative involucre"—a vase-shaped shell of bright "petals" that encloses the tight central cluster of flowers. Those bright, tongue-shaped structures are obviously not petals—they are too sturdy for that—and yet they are too showy to be called leaves. They are called bracts.

The signature species for this group, and a flower that grows spectacularly well in Hawai'i, is *Protea cynaroides*, the so-called king protea. Other members of the genus *Protea* have their own royal designations; for example, queen, duchess, princess, prince, and baron. Proteas with furry or feathery bracts are often called minks.

LEFT: *This is a bud of Protea 'Mayday', one of the most popu-lar varieties grown in Hawai'i. A cross between P. magnifica and P. neriifolia, 'Mayday' blooms for a long time—from winter through spring.  The central flower dome is a rich wine red.*

*RIGHT: Maui grower Jim Heid brought this beautiful plant to Hawai'i from its home in South Africa.  Protea 'Regina' has a long, cylindrical flower head colored fuchsia-magenta throughout.  'Regina' is a hybrid of P. neriifolia and P. obtusifolia.*

*LEFT: This 'Susara' is ripe for cutting.  The flowers are just about to reflex.*

The *Protea* flower opens in several stages. At first the bracts completely enclose the inflorescence. As the configuration matures, the bracts widen, revealing a tight, furry globe formed by a huddle of hundreds of perianths. Within each perianth is a growing style—the long, prong-like female organ that strains to break free.

In the wild, members of the genus *Protea* are pollinated mainly by the sugarbirds of South Africa. Attracted by nectar that they find at the base of each perianth, these birds dive their beaks into the thick of the flower mass and come away with their heads dusted in pollen. Mice and insects are other, less frequent pollinators.

*LEFT: What Hawai'i growers call "minks," the South Africans call "bearded sugarbushes." Those beards are distinctive in this 'Rose Mink,' a New Zealand cultivar that results from the cross of* Protea neriifolia *and* P. laurifolia.
*RIGHT: This hybrid of the species* Protea eximea *shows the typical habit of the "duchess" pro-teas—the bracts are spoon-shaped, tapering at the base.*

# Leucospermum

These classy flowers are all style—that is, all styles. In other words, their airy, globular heads are formed primarily by the long, sprout-like female structures, each one ending in a bulbous knob called a pollen presenter. It's easy to see why this genus is known rather universally by the common name "pincushions." Forty-eight species of *Leucospermum* evolved in the Cape region of South Africa.

At the crowded flower base, the seeds ripen in a fuzz of white threads—hence the name "leuco-spermum," which means white seed.

In this genus, the thick base of the blossom, the receptacle, is often cylindrical or conical.

Unlike flowers of the genus *Protea*, which rely on their showy bracts for visual appeal, leucospermums put all their art into the coloration of the flowers themselves as well as the graceful lines of each curving element.

**Leucospermum oleifolium** *is finding its place in the repertoire of Hawai'i's lei makers, in part because this flower looks similar to the beloved native flower, 'ōhi'a lehua. (The two plants are not related.) Flowers start out yellow and redden with age to deep crimson. This is a good landscaping plant, growing to three feet tall with a long blooming season.*

*ABOVE:* Leucospermum mundii *is an excellent lei flower, one to two inches long in clusters of three to ten on a low-growing, gray-foliaged shrub. In its native Australia this plant is gaining popularity as a potted plant and as a groundcover.*

*RIGHT: University of Hawai'i hybrid 243 is now known as 'Nora Leonhardt.' Dr. Kenneth William Leonhardt, principal investigator for the UH College of Tropical Agriculture and Human Resources, named this beauty in honor of his mother.*

ABOVE: Leucospermum reflexum *at the very start of its blossoming.*

LEFT: *Again, but now mature. Because this flower takes such a radical approach to its reflexing, Hawai'i growers call this the "skyrocket pin." This is one of South Africa's true native species. The odd flower form tends to disqualify it for arrangements, but* L. reflexum *makes a hardy landscape shrub, growing ten to twelve feet tall with small gray-green leaves held close to the stems.*

# Leucadendron

The handsome "silver tree" shown on this page has given its name to an entire genus of proteas. The tree also indicates the distinct appeal of this particular group—the beauty of its leaves.

The scientific name of this tree, *Leucadendron argenteum*, makes the same point twice: "leuca-dendron" means white tree; "argent" means silver. The leucadendrons as a group have chosen to downplay the floral fireworks that we associate with other proteas. Instead, they emphasize the subtler beauty of foliage.

Despite the name, whiteness is not exactly the point with leucadendrons. The silver tree is unique in this genus for its most obvious trait—the reflective leaves covered with a fur of soft, white hairs. (The fur protects the leaves from drying out in harsh sunlight.) But other leucadendrons favor different foliage effects—such as the soft glow of sunshine yellow or smoldering flares of sunset red. Their primary appeal is the architectural elegance of softly shaded leaves around a cone-like floral head.

Leucadendrons are remarkable among the proteas in that individual plants come in separate sexes, male and female. Regardless of the plant's gender, the firm, spherical cones sitting like gigantic gems in the heart of a glowing foliar collar create a botanical effect you won't find anywhere else on Earth.

*ABOVE: When protea growers from around the world visit Valley View Protea Farm in Kula, they gasp at the sight of this enormous silver tree. Valley View owner Corintha Pohle provides a sense of scale by standing in the foreground.*
*FAR LEFT: Leucadendron argenteum, the silver tree, exemplifies the main appeal of the leucadendron tribe—attractive foliage. Unique to this particular species are the sunlight-reflecting white hairs, designed to prevent dehydration. Hawai'i's native silversword (unrelated to proteas) employs this same survival tactic.*

The red-tipped leucadendrons are staples of the protea trade. The three shown on this page are closely related, all variations of the species Leucadendron salignum.

TOP LEFT:  A seedling of 'Red Devil' with darker hues.

TOP RIGHT:  'Jester,' a white-streaked sport of the popular 'Safari Sunset.'

BOTTOM:  'Red Devil.'

FAR LEFT: Pictured here is a male flower of Leucadendron discolor, a spring-flowering shrub that grows four to six feet tall.  The flower cone pokes up like a strawberry in a cream-colored basket.

ABOVE: 'Jester,' a leucadendron variety from New Zealand, gives a tricolor effect—pink, cream, and green. These flowers are all females.

RIGHT: Although the flowers of this male Leucadendron stelligerum have spent their energy, the collars of foliage continue to flame. Flowers like this are often used in Hawaiian haku lei—a intricately braided crown that retain its beauty as it drys.

FAR RIGHT: A cluster of cool candles whose flames refuse to die.

# Banksia

The genus *Banksia* includes seventy-three species, all of which originated in Australia. As with the leucospermums, the inflorescence of these durable shrubs consists entirely of the orchestration of flower parts—no bracts, no colored leaves. Unlike leucospermums, however, the banksias invest a tremendous amount of energy in building up the receptacle. Most of these inflorescences look like corn cobs—tall, cylindrical, and hard at the core. Even the more acorn-shaped blooms are constructed around a dramatic, woody cone.

*FAR LEFT: Banksia occidentalis, or red swamp banksia, is a slender-stemmed tree that grows to twenty feet tall. The plant is prized almost as much for its thready foliage as for its orange-red flowers of the classic banksia design.*

*LEFT: This Australian group turns the protea's thick receptacle into a jutting spike. Banksia menziesii blooms on a crooked, gnarled tree that can reach forty feet high. Flowering spikes are three to five inches long and nearly as wide. They open silver and wine red, eventually reflexing masses of golden styles starting from the bottom up.*

Because banksias are so columnar, the flowers characteristically line up in vertical rows, emphasizing the corn-on-the-cob look. In many banksias, the styles will stay trapped at the tip so long that they will loop out like stiff shoelace knots. The contrast of red and white in columnar rows almost obliterates the awareness that we're looking at natural flowers; rather, these seem to be computer-generated sculptures. Such costly creations grow on leather-leaved shrubs that fight for survival in the scorching conditions of Australia. In this way, banksias take the proteaceous zest for life to the natural extreme.

*FAR LEFT: Banksia speciosa, the showy banksia, bears blossoms up to six inches long and nearly as wide. This is a summer to autumn bloomer. The shrubs are easy to grow and reach as tall as fifteen feet. New buds are wooly white, turning chartreuse, then lemon-colored as the styles reflex.*
*ABOVE: The bud of a Banksia baxteri blossom. This one is a common ingredient of any mixed protea bouquet. The flowers and zigzag leaves are relatively compact. Like all the banksias shown here, they come from Western Australia.*
*LEFT: Banksia baxteri, shown in bud, has ripened and is almost ready for harvest.*

*FAR LEFT:  Nature's design sense boggles the human imagination. These blossoms of* Banksia coccinea, *the scarlet banksia, illustrate the signature qualities of this protea genus – a barrel-shaped inflorescence, with individual flowers mounted on a woody cone in corn-cob-like rows.*
*LEFT: A good look at* Banksia coccinea *will keep you gawking for a long time. The male flower parts are white. The longer female ones are intensely red. A general reluctance to reflex keeps these structures looped back in on themselves.*
*BELOW: Delicate variations of line and form ornament an almost club-like receptacle.*

The land of kangaroos has produced many novel variations on the protea formula. The two flowers pictured on these pages are not banksias—but, like banksias, they evolved in Australia.

ABOVE: Telopia is a genus of four species endemic to New South Wales, Victoria, and Tasmania. The brilliant flowers of these tall, robust shrubs bloom bright red at Christmastime. People call this "a pincushion on steroids."

RIGHT: The golden emperor, Dryandra formosa, is loved just as much for its narrow, dark green, saw-edged foliage as for its rich bronze flower heads. Crafters use the dryandra flowers to make wreaths and dolls (see chapter 8). The genus Dryandra contains many striking ornamental shrubs that have not yet found their place in general cultivation.

Proteas in Hawai‘i

The introduction of these peculiar natives to the attention of the modern world didn't begin in South Africa until 1930. As the world's curiosity turned to desire, proteas started appearing in the flower markets of Amsterdam and other European cities. It was in the 1960s that protea-growing as an industry developed a good set of legs and began traveling the globe. In other words, the protea trade is still a child. That's why the product still strikes people as extraterrestrial—although, in reality, it is an earthly wonder just as distinct and appropriate as a rose, an orchid, or an Easter lily.

The cut-flower trade in proteas began with the simple act of gathering wildflowers from their natural setting in the fynbos. Then, in the late 1940s, South African farmers such as Frank Batchelor began cultivating natural hybrids within the controlled conditions of their own fields and started setting the first standards for widespread marketing of the blooms. South Africa continues to be the world leader in this trade.

But proteas have a way of exciting people's interest. By the time that the South Africa Wildflower Growers Association had formed in 1965, floral pioneers were starting to grow protea in just about every climate suited to the rather narrow requirements of this "Mediterranean" clan. Today you will find protea farms in New

*FAR LEFT: Proteas found their place in the Hawaiian sun only recently. It wasn't until the 1970s that island farmers, encouraged by the University of Hawai'i, started investing serious efforts in these unusual crops.*

Zealand and in Australia, particularly in the Melbourne region. You also will find them in Zimbabwe, Israel, the south of France, Portugal, California, Chile, and on Tenerife in the Canary Islands.

The introduction of proteas to Hawai'i can be credited to one man, Dr. Phil Parvin. A horticultural specialist at the University of California at Davis, Parvin first came to Maui on vacation with his wife in 1966. They fell in love with the island, recognizing it as their "spiritual home in the universe." Two years later, Parvin was offered a position as horticulturist at the University of Hawai'i's Maui Agricultural Research Center in Kula, and he snatched it. Parvin's assignment was to experiment with new floral crops for Hawai'i. When he arrived, he noticed a few dozen protea bushes growing in a corner of the Kula Station's fields. He decided to give these odd florals the same experience he was having—the chance to flourish in the bright Hawaiian sun.

Today, not much more than thirty years later, Hawai'i has 177 acres dedicated to protea production. Some of this cultivation takes place on the island of Hawai'i (aka the Big Island), where growers are experimenting with lava cinders as a planting medium. But most of Hawai'i's proteas grow in Maui's Kula district within a few miles of the site of Parvin's first experiments.

These are small farms; the largest is Jim Heid's Kula Vista Farm with eighty acres in cultivation. As it is elsewhere in the world, protea production in Hawai'i is essentially a family business, perpetuated through the daily hard work of key individuals who foster a personal zeal for these compelling plants.

*Dr. Phil Parvin was a pioneer in the development of Hawai'i's protea floriculture industry. He is shown here while on a nostalgic return visit to Maui in 2002. Other principal figures in Hawai'i protea development are Dr. Stephen Ferreira, Dr. Richard Criley, Dr. John Cho, Dr. Kenneth William Leonhardt, Norman Nagata, and Dr. Phil Ito of the UH Hilo campus.*

Though the farms are small, productivity is high. In 2001, the state sold more than $1.7 million worth of proteas, and the demand continues to outpace supply. Working with the University of Hawai'i, these farmers are constantly experimenting to find proteas that best fit local growing conditions as well as the tastes of the flower-loving public. During the first couple years of the new millennium, the U.H. College of Tropical Agriculture and Human Resources introduced forty entirely new hybrids of leucospermum, or "pincushions." Clearly, protea is a Hawaiian crop with a bright future.

*South Africa's king proteas look right at home under the exuberant, cloud-daubed skies of the Hawaiian Islands. The man holding these king proteas is Neil Waldow, an owner of Kula Vista Protea, the largest protea farm in Hawai'i.*

FAR RIGHT: Leucospermum 'High Gold,' a cross between L. cordifolium 'Yellow Bird' and L. patersonii, has become one of the most widely grown "pincushions" in the world cut-flower trade. Introduced in 1991, 'High Gold' is the first great hybrid to come from the protea developers of Zimbabwe.

In 2002, Maui growers hosted the biennial get-together of the International Protea Association (IPA). Delegates came from all the fynbos-type regions of the world. They bunked at the Renaissance Wailea Beach Resort and spent their days in what must be an exotic location for farmers—indoors. Between lectures on soil micronutrients and the detection of witches' broom disease, they shared their stories of struggle.

The Maui growers had survived four years of drought, but the growers from Zimbabwe were contending with political upheaval and chaotic inflation. A woman from Australia reported not only drought but also hail the size of cricket balls and Christmas brushfires in New South Wales. Even so, she admitted her addiction to protea: "The thing about proteas is that while you grow them, you have to look at them. You develop an addiction to caring about them. And so you keep planting even though the worst disasters loom."

Then the delegates got a day outside to visit the Maui protea farms. Dressed in their crisp, new aloha wear, they found themselves at Kula Vista Farm getting hoisted by hydraulic lift into the back of a stake-sided flatbed truck. In the far distance, the sea beat against the shore and the West Maui Mountains wore a wide turban of clouds. The truck wobbled and jolted down steep dirt tracks between sections of hardy shrubs, some blooming, some quiescent. Growers swapped information about leucadendron varieties and pruning strategies. The truck lurched, and they clutched the wobbling stake sides. People who had looked shy and awkward at the

resort while gripping china cups with weak coffee now grabbed the nearest support and held on tight with peals of laughter. "These are lovely fields," shouted a woman from New Zealand.

With proteas, in Hawai'i and everywhere else, familiarity breeds love.

LEFT: King proteas clamor for attention at this annual flower festival put on by the residents of Ha'ikū, Maui.
FAR LEFT: The charm of the panorama competes with the beauty of these "pincushions" at the University of Hawai'i's Agricultural Research Center in Kula, Maui. In the distance—deeply curved Mā'alaea Bay and the foothills of the leeward West Maui Mountains.

Gardening with Proteas

If your garden at home provides the conditions reminiscent of the proteas' natural "Mediterranean" ecology, you might enjoy cultivating these handsome mid-size shrubs.

In nature, they thrive in inhospitable conditions, poor subsoil, and minimum water. But you don't need to make them suffer. They do respond to care. No matter what you do, though, they tend to be location peculiar—succeeding in one part of the garden but not in another. Be prepared to experiment.

Most important, proteas need well-drained soil. Sandy or even gravelly earth is best. They tend to like their soil on the acidic side. Experiments by Dr. James Martin at University of California at Riverside showed that the best results came in soils of pH 5.0 to 5.5. Gardeners in areas with alkaline conditions, characteristic of California and Israel for example, sometimes acidify their soil with the addition of sulphur, aluminum sulphate, or peat moss.

Most proteas are drought-resistant. Water them at ground level, not by overhead sprinkling. The leaves have evolved to withstand the parching effects of strong mountain breezes. They need fresh air and can't stand the cloying humidity favored by tropicals. It's best not to put them against a wall where the air doesn't circulate freely. Plant where you would grow roses—an open, sunny area with at least six hours of sunlight a day.

*FAR LEFT: Like many members of the family Proteaceae—given "Mediterranean" conditions—*Leucospermum reflexum *does well in the garden.*

*ABOVE: Natural inhabitants of dry mountains, proteas take poorly to overhead watering and soggy conditions.*

*ABOVE: Happy pincushions - Happy gardener.*
*RIGHT: An early disbudding of leucospermum stems results in a crop like this—singular blossoms on exceptionally sturdy stems.*

Most proteas can't bear frost. If you live in an area that freezes, your top priority should be a warm, protected spot.

Leucospermums tend to be more sensitive to frost than members of the genus *Protea*. Some leucadendrons can withstand cold; others, such as the silver tree (*Leucadendron argenteum*) are quickly damaged by frost, especially when the plants are young. On chilly nights, cover small plants with a cardboard box. Once they have wood in the stem (generally after the first couple of years), they can withstand a cold snap.

Many gardeners mulch their plants to conserve water and keep the roots cool. But take care to keep the crowns of the plant bare and allow the soil to breathe. Although proteas are fairly bug-resistant, they are susceptible to fungus diseases.

Pruning keeps the foliage compact; some proteas grow leggy and bloom out of reach if you let them. Trim off the flowers when they finish. There's no reason to let the plant dissipate its energy in seed production. A good after-bloom trim, removing dead material and tired branches, tends to rejuvenate the plant.

You might choose to disbud the leucospermums when they form double or triple flower stalks. This gives you bigger single blooms. But wait till all danger of frost is gone; the early bud is the first to be nipped by cold.

Caring for
Your Bouquet

The sight of a packing shed at one of Hawaii's protea farms is enough to make you dizzy—bundles of kings and minks, pincushions, leucadendrons and banksias seem to spin and sizzle in a rainbow of colors from reds, golds, and oranges to the odd fellows clad in black or even green. Meanwhile, the packers are grading the

*LEFT: The packing shed at Maui's Kula Vista Farm is always crowded with color. Here, king proteas fresh from the field outside are ready for a ride on a jet.*

just-cut stems. "Premiums" are eighteen inches long; "standards" are at least a foot long. Then the blooms are placed carefully—very carefully—into sturdy shipping boxes, the flowers interlocked to keep them from jostling during transit. The packers fill any empty spaces with soft, absorbent material, usually newspaper, to keep the drought-accustomed tissues free from contact with humidity.

Protea flowers handled like this will travel well. Even several days in the shipping carton will fail to dull their fresh brilliance. Their sturdy heritage makes them some of the most reliable and robust commodities in the international cut-flower trade.

*ABOVE: Packing is a craft in itself. This woman is packing a shipment of 'Kathryn' leucospermums. The bucket in the foreground holds two kinds of banksias—B. coccinea and B. menziesii. "Mink" proteas crowd the buckets behind.*

83

Proteas are ever-flowers. Handled properly, they can last two or three weeks in your vase. Then they don't die—they dry. They retain their architecture and to some extent even their color. When you assemble them in dry arrangements, they are as permanent as almost anything the botanical world provides.

When you receive your box of proteas, open it immediately. Carefully lift out the flowers one at a time and trim about half an inch of stem off each one. It doesn't hurt to add some floral preservative to the water in your vase. Handle the blossoms delicately and don't wet them. Keep water off the leaves.

Although proteas have their own unique look, don't be shy about mixing them in the vase with other effects. Let the creative possibilities start presenting themselves. Put leucospermums together with Iceland poppies, or a branch of bougainvillea, or even a few artfully chosen yellow roses. Suddenly these other flowers start to reveal their own forgotten wild beauty.

Go into your yard and select twisted branches, pine tufts, bamboo stalks…. Items that you never before brought inside your home now look right—now that proteas have opened the door to a new kind of beauty. Be bold with your designs. Proteas allow you to see the authentic beauty of the entire botanical world.

While the bouquet is still fresh, change the water regularly. Protea stems are thirsty. As with any flower, try to keep them away from direct sunlight. The flower heads will continue to mature and open. If the leaves start to change color, don't be alarmed. This just means that flowers have begun taking on their "everlasting" form.

*LEFT: As they hang drying from wire netting, protea flowers undergo a subtle transformation.*

When your proteas start drying, empty the water out of the vase and let them harden right where they stand. Better yet, hang them upside-down in a dark place. Then when they have completely changed, give them a second life in a new type of arrangement—mix them with other dried stems and branches, seed pods, or even driftwood.

You can enhance proteas' natural ability to outlast mortality. Pick up some glycerine at the drugstore. Mix one part glycerine with three parts water, and set the stems in this solution, first pounding the stem-ends a little to promote intake. Let the flowers absorb this liquid for a couple of days, then hang them upside-down in the dark.

If you enjoy crafts, use your dried flowers as raw materials for sculptural inventions. By themselves or in combination with other natural materials, proteas make fascinating elements in wreaths, ornaments, dolls, and other creations.

Hawai'i is the home of the flower lei and of many native traditions based on manual dexterity—featherwork, fiber-weaving, net-making, quilting, and so on. Naturally, you'll find many people in the Islands today who are making careers out of their artful inventions with these newcomers to Polynesia.

When protea blossoms find their ultimate place in a timeless wreath, they complete the promise of their first appearance. They finish a story that began in Gondwanaland and triumphed over a thousand

*BELOW: This wreath is made of various protea elements fixed with a hot glue gun to a store-bought grapevine frame. The combination includes small buds of the 'Pink Ice' protea, flowers of the 'Safari Sunset' leucadendron, dryandra, and the foliage of Banksia occidentalis.*
*RIGHT: A Maui woman in her eighties crafts these little dolls. The hair is made of "mink" proteas, trimmed. The dark mink "beards" provide material for the dolls' eyes.*

adversities. They remind us that nature is a creative, inspiring, and perennial force. By the sheer power of their floral enthusiasm, they represent a special kind of connection—a bond with Hawai'i, a link to the past, and a bridge between the outer world of our natural home and the inner world of domestic life.

89

*Cori Pohle of Valley View Protea Farm, Kula, and her daughter Lori Güntzel, are justifiably proud of the sumptuous wreaths they make.*

# How to make a wreath

"To me, it's like painting—but with a palette of flowers," says Cori Pohle, speaking of the gigantic wreaths that she and her daughter Lori create at their small protea farm in Kula, Maui.

They begin with premade wheels of reinforced Styrofoam, prepping them with tufts of dryandra foliage. To fix the elements in place, they dip the stems in a hot glue pot. (A glue gun works as well, though the labor is a bit more tedious.) Then they push the stems into the Styrofoam form—filling the outside and inside rims three rows deep—and let them cool.

Covering the face of the wreath requires a meditation on design, symmetry, and color. "It's all about unity and variety," Cori says. "Don't put the same textures together." For their work, they favor mink proteas. They reckon that thirty-five to forty minks are needed to complete the surface.

To keep herself supplied with wreath-making materials, Cori has rigged up an ingenious drying room. Its ceiling is lined with poultry netting. When Cori gets a new batch of fresh proteas, she cuts off the stem of each flower and plunges a stiff wire into the thick receptacle. By bending the other end of the wire, she can hook the wire onto the poultry netting and let the flower hang while it dries—about three weeks. (Her drying-room ceiling is pictured on page 84.)

The job of fastening the minks to the face of the wreath is a simple matter of cutting the wire to two inches, dipping in hot glue, and sticking in place. Not just minks, though—Cori's palette is broad. The wreath pictured on page 94 includes two species of *Protea*, several leucadendrons, dryandra, and a number of *Banksia occidentalis* flowers (many cut in half). To fill the small patches, she uses German statice, strawflowers, yarrow, lichens, and leaves of the silver tree. Of course, anything at hand is fair game for such craft, from pinecones to fall leaves. If Styrofoam forms are hard to find, grapevine works just as well. Any craft shop will provide inspiration.

A wreath like this will hold its color for a couple of years—more or less, depending largely on the amount of exposure to light. Hanging it on a sunlit wall will hasten the process. The conservative approach is to store it in darkness for display on special occasions.

To learn more about the proteas of Hawai'i—and best of all to order some for yourself or the people you love—go to the following websites:

Hawai'i Tropical Flower Council: www.htfc.com

Protea Growers Association of Hawai'i:  www.pgah.org

Maui Flower Growers Association:  www.mauiflower.com

# Paul Wood

In the early 1990s, Paul Wood left his work as a full-time English/theater arts teacher to pursue a career as an independent writer and editor. He's the author of two story collections, *Four Wheels Five Corners,* 1996, and *False Confessions,* 2002, and he wrote the travel book *Fodor's Escape to the Hawaiian Islands* 2001. His feature journalism is widely published; national credits include *Islands, Preservation*, and *ARTnews* magazines. With this and other plant-based publications for Island Heritage, he returns to the passion for botany that marked his early twenties, when he worked as an herbarium curator, a state-certified nurseryman, and a landscape contractor.

# Ron Dahlquist

Ron Dahlquist sold his first picture to a small surfing publication almost thirty years ago. Today he is a nationally acclaimed photographer whose repertoire ranges from action sports to sensitive pictures of the environment and worldwide travel. His images have appeared in such publications as *Life, Time, National Geographic, World, Forbes, Esquire, Islands, Condé Nast Traveler, Vanity Fair, Outside, Ski, Surfer's Journal, Snowboarder,* and *Windsurfer.* His coffee table book *Under a Maui Sun* was released at the end of 2000. A Maui resident, he has long held a photographer's fascination for the design and color of Hawai'i's protea blooms.

**Art prints from the photography in this book are available by contacting www.rondahlquist.com.**

# Big Island

**Big Island Flower Company**
92-8391 Pineapple Pkwy.
Ocean View, HI 96737
808-939-9043, 800-574-4336 toll free
www.bigislandflower.com

**Flowers & Joys**
4-1302 Kuhio Hwy.
Kapa'a, Kaua'i 96746
808-822-1569

**Hawaiian Flowers**
94-2166 South Point Road
Nā'ālehu, HI 96772
808-929-9737
www.shiphawaiianflowers.com

**Tradewind Tropicals**
296 Center Lane
Pāhoa, HI 96778
800-890-4629 toll free
www.1800aloha.com

**Green Point Nursery**
811 Kealaka'i St.
Hilo, HI 96720
808-959-3535

# Maui

**Anuhea Farms**
3643B Baldwin Ave.
Makawao, Maui, HI 96768
808-572-6877, 888-325-1988 toll free
www.anuheaflowers.com

**Island Flower Design**
1265 Pūlehu Iki St.
Kula, Maui, HI 96790
808-878-6059, 888-550-8338 toll free
www.sendtropicalflowers.com

**Kula Vista Protea Farm**
No street address available.
See mile marker #5 on Haleakalā Hwy.
808-878-3251, 888-878-3251 toll free
www.kulavistaprotea.com

**Maui Floral**
760 Copp Road
Kula, Maui, HI 96790
808-878-1218, 888-543-2727 toll free
www.mauifloral.com

**Proteas of Hawai'i**
417 Mauna Place
Kula, Maui, HI 96790
808-878-2533, 800-367-7768 toll free
www.proteasofhawaii.com

**Sunrise Protea Farm**
16157 Haleakalā Hwy.
Kula, Maui, HI 96790
808-876-0200, 800-222-2797 toll free
www.sunriseprotea.com

**Sunset Tropicals & Davis Farms**
1018 Waipoli Road
Kula, Maui, HI 96790
808-878-1211

**Upcountry Harvest Gift Shop**
15200 Haleakalā Hwy.
Kula, Maui, HI 96790
800-575-6470 toll free
www.upcountryharvest.com

# Dried Protea

**Valley View Protea Farm**
17100 Haleakalā Hwy.
Kula, Maui, HI 69790
808-878-2758
www.valleyviewprotea.com